The Seasons of Time

TANKA POETRY OF ANCIENT JAPAN

edited by *Virginia Olsen Baron*
illustrated by *Yasuhide Kobashi*

More than a thousand years ago the Emperor of
Japan commanded that the best poetry written
in his domain since the beginning of recorded
history be collected for his Imperial enjoyment.
The poet Ki no Tsurayuki was ordered to
undertake the work and he produced the
Kokinshū, or *Collection of Ancient and Modern
Poems.* A hundred and fifty years earlier a
collection had been made called the *Manyōshū,*
or *Collection of a Myriad Leaves.* Most of the
poems in this volume were selected from these
ancient compilations.

In both collections there are some poems drawn
from folklore ; others are by the greatest poets
of their day. Some are by priests, others by
shoguns. Some are by courtiers and at least one
is ''by a lady whose name we do not know.'' All
of them, in Tsurayuki's words, ''have their roots
in the human heart and flourish in the countless
leaves of words.''

The tanka form predates the more familiar
haiku by almost a thousand years and is still the
most popular form in modern Japanese poetry.
While tanka poetry has the same directness and

The Seasons of Time

TANKA POETRY OF ANCIENT JAPAN

The Seasons of Time

TANKA POETRY OF ANCIENT JAPAN edited by Virginia Olsen Baron

illustrated by Yasuhide Kobashi

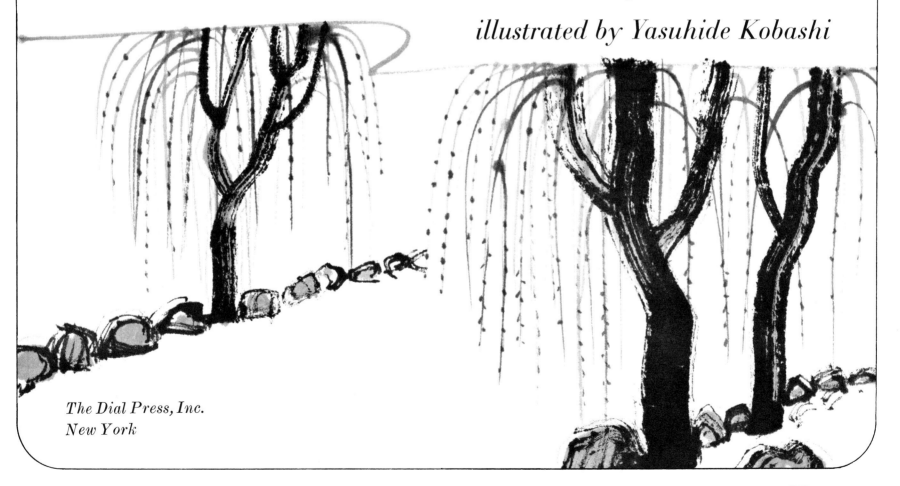

The Dial Press, Inc.
New York

*This book is dedicated to
everyone under the moon in
the wide heaven*

Introduction

What has changed in our world since the seventh and eighth centuries? One's first answer might be "everything," followed immediately by a second answer, "nothing." Perhaps the true answer dwells somewhere in the land between.

Most of the poems in this anthology were first collected for the *Manyōshū (Collection of a Myriad Leaves)* compiled in or about the year 759, and for the *Kokinshū* collection compiled in about 905. Some of the poems date back to the fourth or fifth century, while others were written as late as the twelfth century. What is amazing is that this ancient Japanese poetry is as modern as e. e. cummings, as succinct as Emily Dickinson, as close to us as Carl Sandburg and Robert Frost. And all of this in spite of the imperfections necessitated by translation not only from another language very different in origin from our own but from an ancient form of that language. It is like reading *Beowulf* today except that, astonishingly, the Japanese poets who flourished at the same time in another tradition seem much less remote to us.

In the preface to the *Kokinshū (Collection of Ancient and Modern Poems)*, Ki no Tsurayuki (884–946), who collected the poems at the Imperial command of the Emperor Daigo, says that, "The poetry of Japan has its roots in the human heart and flourishes in the countless leaves of words." It should not be forgotten that the Japanese poets, whether courtiers or peasants, were not writing primitive poetry even in the seventh century. They wrote from a sense of heritage which included a deep understanding of nature and their immediate world. Many of the poets were acquainted with the teachings of Confucius and Buddha, while others, not connected with court life, were familiar with the traditional symbols of Japanese poetry and song. Some of the anonymous poems fall into the realm of folk songs, handed down orally from one generation to another.

Although the seasons in Japan do not change abruptly, each is clearly delineated from the others and each is associated with its own distinct poetic sentiments and has a poetic language of its own. It is of benefit for the western reader to have a slight introduction to the meanings evoked in the Japanese mind by the mention of certain birds, beasts, insects, flowers, and other manifestations of nature which have accompanied their emotional life through the centuries. These form a key, not altogether necessary but enriching, to the enjoyment of Japanese poetry.

One ought to know that the *uguisu*, sometimes called a nightingale and sometimes called a warbler, is a harbinger of spring as are our robins; the *nué*, a night thrush, signals a plaintive note; and when the sound of singing frogs is heard, spring is almost over. The cuckoo, a symbol of true love, brings summer, while the mournful shrilling of the cicadas warns that summer is dying. The sounds of wild geese crying, the stag calling its mate, crickets chirping in the garden tell the reader that winter draws near. Sanderlings on beaches, wild ducks among the reeds, and the crane's call are sad and sorrowful reminders of melancholy winter.

Plum blossoms *(ume)* are the earliest flower of spring and the symbol of new love beginning; they fall with the last snowflakes. Then come peach blossoms and, after that, the most beloved, cherry blossoms, the symbol both for beauty and for life itself. Spring is finally here covering the ground with violets while the willows turn green overhead. But when the chirping of autumn crickets is heard, a longing for a distant home and friends is awakened. The pine tree represents nobility and the chrysanthemum speaks for autumn and early winter. It is also the personal emblem of the emperor (named so in 797 by the Mikado, who decreed that it could only be used by royalty). Fir trees and heron signify long life or anything enduring. And above all, the moon is a mirror to reflect the face of one's beloved, however near or far away. Japanese poetry has a gentle way of reminding us of the omnipresent sense of mutual sympathy existing between man and nature. In the early nineteenth century we find Wordsworth echoing the same feelings in his "Ode: Intimations of Immortality."

Thanks to the human heart by which we live,
Thanks to its tenderness, its joys and fears,
To me the meanest flower that blows can give
Thoughts that do often lie too deep for tears.

The "tanka" or "short-song" was the poetic form most prevalent in early Japanese poetry collections and is still the most popular form in modern Japan. In spirit, it has been likened to our sonnet although it is only about a third as long. The tanka is a verse of five lines of 5-7-5-7-7 syllables. Usually Japanese verse is composed of combinations of syllables in fives and sevens. (The hokku, or haiku, which came into use in the seventeenth century, contains seventeen syllables in lines of 5-7-5.) The number of syllables is the only principle of Japanese poetry. There is no note taken of stress, pitch, length of syllables, or rhyme. All but one of the poems in this collection are written in *tanka* form. Although there were longer poems called *naga-uta* in the early collections, they were few in proportion to tanka (the *Manyōshū* contains 4,173 tanka and 324 *naga-uta*) and the form almost disappears after the eighth century.

Translating ancient Japanese texts into modern English is, as we have already noted, difficult. Some of the earlier texts were written completely in Chinese char-acters, others were written in a combination of Chinese and Japanese characters for this was a period of transition in the history of Japan. The Japanese grammatical constructions must be completely reversed in translation in order to make sense in English. The Japanese language is rich in homonyms and many of these double meanings must be sacrificed along with shadings of words which do not exist in English, not to mention the difficulties presented by idioms, rhetorical devices, and the like which are often stumbling blocks for the translator. In spite of all the difficulties, with only the bare and simple meanings in some cases, and with attempts to remain true to the spirit of the poem in other cases, the poetry emerges as a source of delight and beauty.

Tsurayuki ended his preface to the *Kokinshū* with these words:

Hitomaro is gone. His poetry remains. Time may pass, and seasons change; pleasure and pain may come and go. These poems, written, stand! As the long thread-like leaves of the willow, forever renewed; as the needles of the pine, eternally green; as the tendrils of creepers that cover the fields in endless profusion; as bird-tracks that multiply in the sand by the seashore of time: even so Poetry shall forever last. And men who know its form and feature, and who understand its heart, will worship the poetry of old even as we do the moon in the wide heaven; but will not fail to love as well the poetry of today.[1]

After reading these poems written a thousand years ago, we ask ourselves again, what has changed? Not the birds, not the trees, not the flowers, not the snow, not the rain. Nor the wind, stars, sea, sun, and moon. And not the seasons. Is it only people then, who are different? The poets talked of love and loneliness, of yearnings and sorrows, of dreams and hopes. What has changed, after all?

[1]Translated by C. H. Page in *Japanese Poetry,* page 43.

Each season, more lovely,
Eight thousand kinds of bushes,
Trees and flowers blossom,
And the voices of the singing birds even change.
Each time we hear it with our ears
And see it with our eyes,
And still sighing within, we bend down,
Heartshaken, longing and yearning while living on.
In the dark shade of the trees,
When the fourth moon stands up,
Hidden in the night,
The crying cuckoo should be a real young of the
   nightingale,
As is handed down since olden times.
The young girls will thread the sweetflag
And the orange into chaplets.
Radiant during the whole radiant day,
That cuckoo flies over the many tops of the hills,
Till he faces the moon of early morning,
Going and turning,
He sings resounding.
Should I ever get enough of it?

YAKAMOCHI

Spring

HARU

If it were not for the voice
Of the nightingale,
How would the mountain village
Where the snow is still unmelted
Know the spring?

LADY NAKATSUKASA

With the spreading mists
The treebuds swell in early spring
And wet snow petals fall—
So even my flowerless country village
Already lies beneath its fallen flowers.

TSURAYUKI

Above the water
Gliding softly down the rocks,
The buds of bracken
Burgeoning in tender green—
Spring has come already!

PRINCE SHIKI

With voice unceasing
Sing, O nightingale!
In one year
Even as much as twice
Can Spring come?

FUJIWARA NO OKIKAZE

15

Do those girls set out
On some excursion for young shoots,
That they so gaily beckon,
Waving their white linen sleeves
Toward the green fields of ancient Kasuga?

TSURAYUKI

The wild geese returning
Through the misty sky—
Behold, they look like
A letter written
In faint ink!

TSUMORI KUNIMOTO

Now it is spring—
And across the moors the haze
Stretches heavily—
And within these rays at sunset,
A warbler fills the radiant mist with song.

YAKAMOCHI

16

...もせす
...に…つ…とちりぬ
…わかすたれぬ…
…ふらむとちりぬ
…うひの
…やまけふこえて
…やめみしぬ
…つはに
…とちりぬるを
…かすたれそ
…とちりぬそて
…ぶらむ
…うゐるお
…うゐるお
…やすふこえて
…ゐめみして
…のもせす
…つとちりぬる
…やかすたれそ
…にゆつとちりぬそて
…ふらむ
…われふらすけふこ

When I went out
In the Spring meadows
To gather violets,
I enjoyed myself
So much that I stayed all night.

AKAHITO

Clear is the bottom of the lake,
That mirrors the wistaria bloom;
And there in those sunken pebbles
I see countless gems.

YAKAMOCHI

In the fields of spring,
The nightingales sing.
To gain their friendship,
The plum blossoms have burst open
In the garden of my house.

ANON.

The spring rain
Which hangs to the branches
Of the green willow
Looks like pearls
Threaded on a string.

LADY ISE

The rotten-wooded willow
At the road side
When spring comes,
Yearns bitterly for old times.

SUGUWARA NO MICHIZANE

Can it be that there is no moon
And that spring is not
The spring of old,
While I alone remain
The same person?

NARIHIRA

In the eternal
Light of the spring day
The flowers fall away
Like the unquiet heart.

KI NO TOMONORI

In one petal of this flower,
I have concealed
Hundreds of words.
Do not think foolishly of them!

HIROTSUGU

Within one petal of this flower,
Hundreds of words
Can surely not be held.
Would it not be broken off?

ANSWER BY THE YOUNG WOMAN
TO WHOM THE POET SENT THE
FLOWER

The cherry blossoms
Of the tenantless house
On the reed plain
Must with an easy heart
Fall in the wind.

YEKEI HOSHI

22

The bridge of dreams
Floating on the brief spring night
Soon breaks off:
Now from the mountaintop a cloud
Takes leave into the open sky.

TEIKA

As now I come
And see the spring day grow to dusk
In the mountain hamlet,
The cherry blossoms fall to earth
At the sounding of a temple's vesper bell.

NŌIN

Mirrored in the waters of the Kamunabi River,
Where the song-frogs call,
Do they bloom now—those flowers of the yellow
    rose?

PRINCE ATSUMI

The flowers to the tree's root,
The birds to their old nest
Have returned;
But whither spring has gone
No man knows.

EMPEROR SŪTOKU

The plum blossoms have opened,
But what is still in bud,
Is my hidden longing.
Does it wait for the snow?

ANON.

Summer

NATSU

In the leafy treetops
Of the summer mountain
The cuckoo calls—
Oh, how far off his echoing voice!

    YAKAMOCHI

On summer nights
When I wonder "Shall I go to bed?"
At the single note sung
By the cuckoo,
Dawn suddenly breaks!

    TSURAYUKI

The men of valor
Have gone to the honorable hunt:
The ladies
Are trailing their red petticoats
Over the clean sea-beach.

    AKAHITO

Here where the wild ducks
Sport in the pond,
The leaves fall from the trees
And float—but no floating heart
Have I who love you true.

TANIHA ŌMÉ

A passing shower
Has fallen on the garden grass;
And I hear the voice
Of the crickets singing—
Autumn is here.

ANON.

Even for the space of a flash
Of lightning
That flashes over the corn ears
Of an autumn field,—
Can I forget you?

ANON.

Turned towards the moon
In the dark night,
The cuckoo's crying voice
Sounds remote and faint.
Is it because my village is so far away?

YAKAMOCHI

After the storm
On Mount Mimuro,
The colored leaves
Float like brocade
On the River Tatsuta.

NŌIN

Standing or sitting,
I know not what to do.
Though I tread the earth,
My heart is in the skies.

ANON.

As I row over the plain
Of the sea and gaze
Into the distance, the waves
Merge with the bright sky.

FUJIWARA NO TADAMICHI

Would my house were on the cliff
Of Suminoye!
I should be happy always watching
The white waves drawing near
To the shore of the open sea.

ANON.

Come, companions!
Quick to Yamato!
The pine on the beach of Mitu
Will wait impatiently for us.

OKURA

Gossip grows like weeds
In a summer meadow.
My girl and I
Sleep arm in arm.

HITOMARO

If only the world
Would always remain this way,
Some fishermen
Drawing a little rowboat
Up the river bank.

MINAMOTO NO SANETOMO

Like my cupped hands
Spilling drops back into the mountain pool
And clouding its pure waters
Before the satisfaction of my thirst,
So have I had to part from you too soon.

TSURAYUKI

We have seen the sun
Make colored banners of the clouds
As it set in the sea—
If only now that darkness falls
The radiant moon will fill the night.

EMPEROR TENCHI

On the sea of heaven the waves of cloud arise,
And the moon's ship is seen sailing
To hide in a forest of stars.

HITOMARO

32

Autumn

AKI

Here where the wild ducks
Sport in the pond,
The leaves fall from the trees
And float—but no floating heart
Have I who love you true.

TANIHA ŌMÉ

A passing shower
Has fallen on the garden grass;
And I hear the voice
Of the crickets singing—
Autumn is here.

ANON.

Even for the space of a flash
Of lightning
That flashes over the corn ears
Of an autumn field,—
Can I forget you?

ANON.

Turned towards the moon
In the dark night,
The cuckoo's crying voice
Sounds remote and faint.
Is it because my village is so far away?

YAKAMOCHI

After the storm
On Mount Mimuro,
The colored leaves
Float like brocade
On the River Tatsuta.

NŌIN

Startled
By a single scream
Of the crane which is reposing
On the surface of the swamp,
All the other birds are crying.

SAIGYO HŌSHI

When I count
The waves illuminated by the moon which shines
On the face of the water,
Tonight indeed must be the very middle of autumn!

MINAMOTO NO SHITAGŌ

Will it go crying
To Yamato?
The Yobuko bird.
Ah, calling it crosses over
The Naka hills of Kisa!

FURUBITO

Out in the marsh reeds
A bird cries out in sorrow,
As though it had recalled
Something better forgotten.

TSURAYUKI

As evening falls,
From along the moors the autumn wind
Blows chill into the heart,
And the quails raise their plaintive cry
In the deep grass of secluded Fukakusa.

SHUNZEI

In the mountain village
The wind rustles the leaves.
Deep in the night, the deer
Cry out beyond the edge of dreams.

MINAMOTO NO MOROTADA

In the empty mountains
The leaves of the bamboo grass
Rustle in the wind.
I think of a girl
Who is not here.

HITOMARO

The deer which lives
On the evergreen mountain
Where there are no autumn leaves
Can know the coming of autumn
Only by its own cry.

ŌNAKATOMI YOSHINOBU

In the evening calm the cranes search for prey,
But when the tide comes in,
The waves of the open sea rise so high
That each calls its own mate.

ANON.

Upon the mountain edge
Noisy as a flock of teal
Though we are walking,
I am lonely, ah!
Because you are not here.

                    EMPEROR OKAMOTO

In the evening
The rice leaves in the garden
Rustle in the autumn wind
That blows through my reed hut.

                    MINAMOTO NO TSUNENOBU

In my loneliness
I step outside my hut and gaze
In quiet reverie,
But everywhere it is the same:
The melancholy autumn dusk.

            RYŌZEN

In a gust of wind the white dew
On the Autumn grass
Scatters like a broken necklace.

                    FUNYA NO ASAYASU

There is a fading time
For blossoming flowers.
But the worthless roots
Of the reeds of the mountains,
Exist a long time!

ANON.

How will you manage
To cross alone
The autumn mountain
Which was so hard to get across
Even when we went the two of us together?

PRINCESS DAIHAKU

While I stay alone,
Feeling weary and forlorn,
Longing after you,
The autumn breeze comes blowing,
And the moon sinks to the west.

ANON.

Winter

FUYU

The white chrysanthemum
Is disguised by the first frost.
If I wanted to pick one
I could find it only by chance.

MITSUNE

Magnificent snow
Has fallen here at my place.
But at your tumbledown old village of Ōhara,
If ever, later it will fall.

EMPEROR TEMMU

It was I who did command
The Dragon God of these hills
To send down the snow,
Whereof a few fragments, perchance,
Were sprinkled over your home.

ANSWER BY THE LADY FUJIWARA

Like a wave crest
Escaped and frozen,
One white egret
Guards the harbor mouth.

EMPEROR UDA

Yonder in the plum tree,
Fluttering from branch to branch,
The warbler sings;
And white on his wings falls
Airy snow.

ANON.

48

This evening so cold and chill
That the mallards' wings are white with frost
As they skim the reedy shore,
How I think of Yamato!

PRINCE SHIKI

When the frost lies white
Upon fields where travelers
Must find their shelter,
O flock of heavenly cranes,
Cover my child with your wings!

ANON.

How sad this road
Covered over with the obscuring snow,
Where not a person passes,
Where not a trace remains to mark the course
Of travel through a world of fading hopes.

MITSUNE

To be old—
Now amid the swirling snow
I understand:
No one comes to visit me;
There is no place to go.

TEIKA

I have always known
That at last I would
Take this road, but yesterday
I did not know that it would be today.

NARIHIRA

This World

YO NO NAKA

To what shall I compare
This world?
To the white wake behind
A ship that has rowed away
At dawn!

MANSEI

As for this world,
That way or this way—
It is the same thing;
For both palace and cottage
Come to nothing in the end.

SEMIMARU

My existence in the world has been
As the reflection of the moon
Which lodges in water
Gathered in the palm of the hand,
About which one doubts whether it is there or not!

TSURAYUKI

A thing which fades
With no outward sign—
Is the flower
Of the heart of man
In this world!

ONO NO KOMACHI

Since I am convinced
That reality is in no way
Real,
How am I to admit
That dreams are dreams?

SAIGYO HŌSHI

One of us may feel
That life holds only pain, and another
That our lot is shameful,
Yet since we are not birds, but men,
We cannot find escape in flight.

OKURA

O pine tree standing
At the side of the stone house,
When I look at you,
It is like seeing face to face
The men of old time.

HAKUTSŪ

58

In my delight to see
The moon come up between the trees,
I wish only that
I might live west of those western hills
And watch its rising sooner still.

BY A COURT LADY WHOSE NAME
WE DO NOT KNOW

How I yearn to be
Unalterably what once I was,
Immovable as a rock,
But because I belong to this world,
There is no stop to time.

OKURA

When I see the pine trees,
Standing along the road in a row,
It is like those,
Whom I left at home,
Seeing me off!

ANON.

Index of Poets